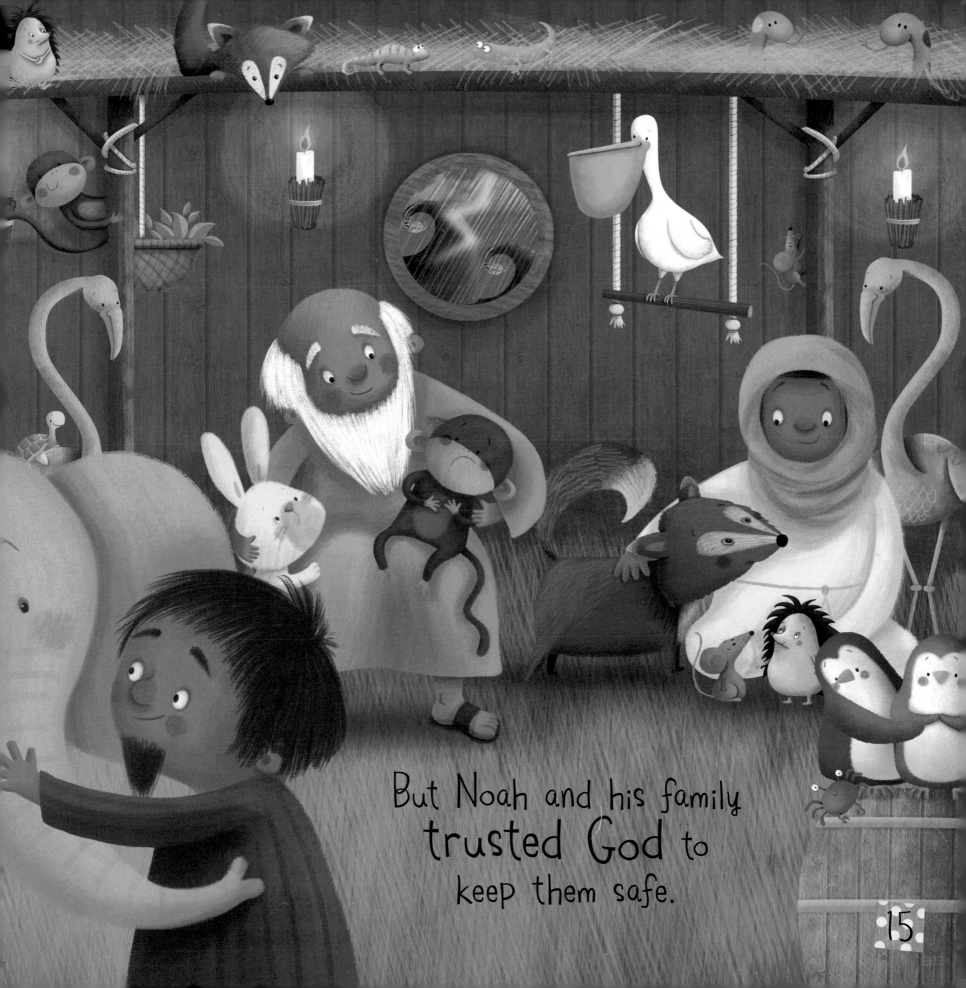

But Noah and his family
trusted God to
keep them safe.

15

It rained and it rained, and the world was **washed clean** by an enormous flood, as God had wished.

Soon even the **highest mountains** were covered by the water, and still the rain came.

It rained for

forty days and forty nights,

then as quickly as it started, it stopped.

Joseph
and his Coat
of Many Colours

There once was a man called Jacob who had twelve sons.

His favourite sons were Joseph and
26 Benjamin, but he **loved** Joseph the most.

When Joseph turned seventeen, Jacob gave him a beautiful **coat** of many different **colours**.

This made Joseph's brothers very **jealous**. 27

Another prisoner told Joseph, "I dreamt I was carrying three baskets of bread, but birds were eating it."

Joseph's face fell, and he said sadly, "In three days' time, you will die."

The dreams came true.

One morning, Pharaoh awoke after two strange dreams.

In the first dream, seven fat COWS were eaten by seven thin cows!

38

In the second dream, seven small, shrivelled ears of **corn** swallowed up seven big, full ears of corn.

Pharaoh's butler remembered Joseph, so Pharaoh sent for him at once.

Moses in the Bulrushes

Long ago in Egypt there lived a group of people called the **Israelites.**

50

They lived **peacefully** among the Egyptian people, where some became rich.

51

Then they wrapped
the baby in a blanket
to keep him warm, and
put him in the basket.

61

Then Miriam and her mother crept down to the river and placed the basket with the sleeping baby among the **tall bulrushes.**

62

The little basket bobbed gently on the water.

Miriam's mother returned home to stop people becoming suspicious. **Miriam hid** in the bulrushes and kept watch over her baby brother.

David and Goliath

Thousands of years ago, in a land called Judea, there lived an Israelite boy called David. He was the youngest of eight brothers.

He spent his days working as a shepherd boy. Even though he was young, David was **brave**. He often fought off bears from his flock.

David walked down to a nearby stream and picked up five smooth **stones**, placing them in his shepherd's pouch.

Then he strode out to meet the giant, whose name was Goliath of Gath.

He only had his slingshot and the stones.